A tenth anniversary
celebration of

A TENTH ANNIVERSARY

CELEBRATION

of

Multicultural

Publishing

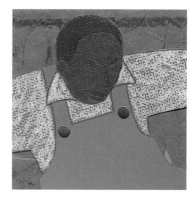

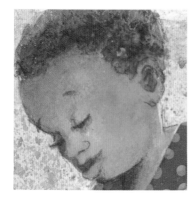

LEE & LOW BOOKS Inc.
New York

Special thanks to the following individuals and organizations whose contributions have been vital to our success: Danny Adlerman, Christy Hale, Tania Garcia, David Neuhaus, Elizabeth Szabla, John Man, South China Printing Company, Publishers Group West, and Whitehurst & Clark. Thanks also to all the supporters who have shared our mission, read our books, and encouraged us to continue, including booksellers, wholesalers, reviewers, review journals, librarians, educators, children, parents, grandparents, and everyone who believes in the power of stories. We could not have done it without you.

Manufactured in China by South China Printing Co.

Book design by Christy Hale
Book production by The Kids at Our House

The display type is set in Stymie Bold
The text is set in Abadi Condensed Light

First Edition

ISBN 1-58430-172-4

Dear Friends,

When we first considered the idea of starting a children's book publishing company in the late 1980s, we had a simple idea: to publish multicultural literature that all children can enjoy. We wanted to create books that were authentic, with a fresh point of view about our diverse society. We did not have prior children's book publishing experience, but through hard work and dedication—and with help from many people—we published our first list of three books in Spring 1993.

Our goal in the beginning was to introduce new voices and talent to the world of children's books, so we focused on working with authors and artists who had not previously been published. As time passed and we became an established company, we also began working with experienced authors and artists who shared our mission. Yet we continue to believe in the importance of bringing fresh perspectives to the children's publishing community, so in 2000 we introduced our New Voices Award for first-time picture book authors of color.

For this anniversary book celebrating our first ten years of publishing, we asked twenty-five of our authors and artists to comment on the impact their books have had on their personal lives and careers. These creative people, as well as all the other talented individuals we have published, have been an integral part of our success. We extend our thanks and appreciation to them, especially for their faith and trust in a small, independent publisher.

As we celebrate our accomplishments with pride and gratitude, we also welcome the challenges ahead. We will continue to publish books that inspire and enrich the lives of children. Thank you for your support, and for being part of our exciting journey.

Regards,

Philip Lee   Thomas Low

Craig Low   Jason Low

Louise E. May   Jennifer Frantz

Abraham Barretto   Willie Jiang

Jennifer Stevens

1993 • Lee & Low Books • 2003

Spring 1993

BASEBALL SAVED US
by **Ken Mochizuki**
illustrated by **Dom Lee**

- Parents' Choice Award
- "Choices," Cooperative Children's Book Center
- Pick of the Lists, *American Bookseller*

"A new dimension in . . . the traditional sports story." —*Booklist*

"Captures the confusion, wonder and terror of a small child in such stunning circumstances with convincing understatement."

—*The New York Times Book Review*

Ken Mochizuki

"Out of nowhere, during August 1991, I received a phone call from a man identifying himself as Philip Lee. He was starting a multicultural picture book company and was looking for writers to produce his first books. Would I be interested?

"He then sent me a magazine article about Kenichi Zenimura, an immigrant from Japan living in Fresno, California. In 1942 Zenimura, along with thousands of others of Japanese descent, was removed from his home along the U.S. west coast and placed in a prison camp. But through ingenious means, Zenimura and his fellow believers in baseball didn't let their location and situation stop them from playing baseball.

"Mr. Lee suggested a nonfiction story about Zenimura. I opted for historical fiction with a young protagonist who hits not only one home run in a critical situation, but two.

"Over the past ten years, I have had a career as an author, and have traveled all over America. I have been to countless schools, libraries, and conferences, where I have met hundreds of students, teachers, readers, and some truly great people. All due to a kid nicknamed 'Shorty' and his two home runs."

Keunhee Lee

Dom Lee

"When I was a child, my father was an artist and life was not easy for my family. We were constantly moving from one home to another, and I never really had the chance to make any friends. Drawing was my only form of entertainment.

"I love painting and drawing, especially in the narrative and realistic forms. I like to tell stories about people through my paintings. When Philip Lee suggested I illustrate *Baseball Saved Us*, I hadn't expected myself to become a children's book illustrator.

"I was very impressed with the manuscript of *Baseball Saved Us*. When I read about the main character's hardships, his obstacles reminded me of my own hard times and, more importantly, the troubles that my family experienced in our first year living in America.

"*Baseball Saved Us* was the first children's book I illustrated, and it was also one of the first published works of Lee & Low Books. I'm glad my first picture book was published by a small group like Lee & Low. As Lee & Low grows, I feel as if I grow too. And because of this project, I was carried over to a new line of work."

Find out more at leeandlow.com/books/baseball.html

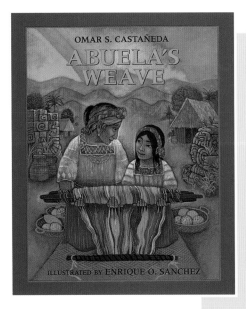

Spring 1993

ABUELA'S WEAVE

by **Omar S. Castañeda**
illustrated by **Enrique O. Sanchez**

- Notable Books for Children, *Smithsonian* magazine
- Parents' Choice Award Honor
- "Choices," Cooperative Children's Book Center

"A story rich in history and family tradition." —*Smithsonian* magazine

"[The] rich narrative effectively evokes the harmonious way of life of many Indian communities in Latin America. . . . A book to be read independently and enjoyed by all children." —*School Library Journal*

Omar Castañeda

was born in Guatemala, the son of renowned philosopher Hector-Neri Castañeda and sculptor Miriam Castañeda. He moved to the United States as a child and grew up attending schools in the Midwest. He went on to write many distinguished works for adults.

Castañeda started writing for children in 1988, and *Abuela's Weave* marked his debut as a picture book author. Castañeda commented that *Abuela's Weave* "continues my work on Guatemala. As a Guatemalan who left the country at a very young age, I seem to be always writing my way back home. In so doing, I have, perhaps, the hope of writing myself, of discovering the many people and histories and traditions that swirl inside me and that beg to be understood.

"In Mayan culture, the image of women weaving on back-strap looms is a powerful allusion to the passing of traditions, the fabric of time, the weaving of generations, the creating of prayers and of worship for the gods. This story conveys in real terms the passing of ancient Mayan traditions from grandmother to granddaughter in a world undergoing rapid change, rapid extinctions."

Omar Castañeda died in 1997.

Amy Walthall

Joan Sanchez

Enrique O. Sanchez

"I have been a fine art painter all my life and had not considered illustrating picture books for children. Then, ten years ago, out of the blue, I was offered the chance to illustrate Omar Castañeda's *Abuela's Weave*.

"I was immediately attracted to this sweet, beautiful, yet strong story. I wanted the design of every picture to speak of the strong bond and love between Esperanza and her grandma. I used different means to connect the ancient Mayan culture with the story's characters, as in the stone steles [monuments] on the cover and the Mayan motifs hidden in the trees' foliage leading down to Grandma as she passes on her knowledge to Esperanza.

"The research for illustrating *Abuela's Weave* spawned an interest in the Mayan and Aztec cultures of Central America and Mexico, and inspired me to travel to those lands.

"Illustrating *Abuela's Weave* was also the beginning of another occupation besides my painting. Since then I have illustrated stories on various themes, but I most enjoy working on stories set in times and environments other than the present.

"It is pleasing to hear children and parents say they read this book over and over."

Spring 1994

BEIN' WITH YOU THIS WAY

by W. Nikola-Lisa
illustrated by **Michael Bryant**

- Reading Magic Award, *Parenting* magazine
- Best Children's Books, *Child* magazine
- Jane Addams Children's Book Award Honor

"This fast-paced, cheerful, rap story is multicultural literature at its best."
—*Child* magazine

"The cheerful faces and colorful outdoor scenes in Bryant's vibrant paintings harmonize so well with the bouncy rapping that children will clamor for an immediate reread."
—*Kirkus Reviews*

W. Nikola-Lisa

Barbara Cooper

"In the fall of 1992 I had traveled to a teaching conference. When I arrived to pick up my registration materials, I was struck by the number of people there, all so different and yet all there for the same reason: to talk about, study, and understand better the world of children and teaching. That was the exact point of inspiration for *Bein' with You This Way*.

"*Bein' with You This Way* opened many doors, enabling me to speak to a variety of groups. Early on, when the book had been out only a year, I was invited to spend the day at a school in Minneapolis. I was unprepared for the students' responses. Each class had been given the book and encouraged to do its own rendition of the story. So instead of me going around to different classrooms giving readings, the students treated me to an entire morning of their presentations in the auditorium. The book was read, sung, danced—you name it. Each class had its own signature way of interpreting the book. I was completely overwhelmed by all the wonderful ways I heard the story presented.

"I don't think I've ever written a book that has touched so many people."

Michael Bryant

"When I was first given the manuscript for *Bein' with You This Way*, I thought I would illustrate a circus scene with a ringmaster and animals learning about differences and similarities. Then one day my four-year-old daughter came home from preschool, where she and a friend had been playing with some dolls. My daughter innocently shared with us that she was white, her friend was white, and their dolls were white. The problem was that we're African American. At that point I realized this story could be a perfect way to teach my daughter about differences among people and how to respect and celebrate those differences. The illustrations actually feature my wife and two daughters and capture a special period in my family life.

"Before working on this book, I didn't consider how important a book can be in someone's life. I've been asked to work on other projects because of *Bein' with You*. And when I visit schools, often I've been greeted by children dressed like the characters in the book. Sometimes there are posters made by the students and sometimes they send letters, all of which I am extremely grateful for."

Find out more at leeandlow.com/books/bein.html

Fall 1994

ZORA HURSTON AND THE CHINABERRY TREE

by **William Miller**
illustrated by **Cornelius Van Wright** *and* **Ying-Hwa Hu**

- *Reading Rainbow* selection
- Notable Social Studies Trade Books for Young People, National Council for the Social Studies and the Children's Book Council
- Pick of the Lists, *American Bookseller*

"[A] lyrical affirmation of life's unlimited potential."

—*The Horn Book Magazine*

"Emphasizes the awareness of family, nature and community that is reflected in [Zora Hurston's] writing." —*The New York Times Book Review*

William Miller

"*Zora Hurston and the Chinaberry Tree* was my first book for children. Originally I had written a poem based on a scene in Hurston's autobiography about her mother's death when Hurston was a young girl. The poem was published in a literary magazine. The biggest challenge was then to make the poem into an accessible story for children. I also wanted to use actual lines and images from the poem. I simply tried to write a book that I would like to read if I were a child.

"When Lee & Low published *Zora*, I suddenly had a new career as a children's book author. I have met so many great people, especially children who have read the book. Children are the best audience. What they say about your writing comes from the heart.

"Even now, many years since the book was published, I meet people who've read and enjoyed it. A child psychologist once told me she keeps a copy of *Zora* in her office. She encourages children who have lost a parent to read it. I can't think of any greater reward than knowing my book has helped a child deal with such a painful loss."

Teresa Rowe/Everlasting Images
Chris Allen

Cornelius Van Wright and Ying-Hwa Hu

"When we read the manuscript for *Zora Hurston and the Chinaberry Tree,* it was exactly what we were looking for as our first picture book project. It was beautifully written and very poetic, with lots of room for image interpretations.

"This was also our first project where we had to do a lot of research. We had never invested so much time, energy, and resources in a single book. We spent a week just trying to track down an actual chinaberry tree (they do not grow in the Northeast).

"The publication of *Zora* was a breakthrough book for us, artistically and commercially. But most important the book opened the door for us to visit children in schools and libraries to see and hear their reactions. One memory that will always stay with us comes from a trip to our local supermarket, where we were shopping with our children. A little girl and her mother stopped us and asked if we were the couple who had illustrated *Zora Hurston and the Chinaberry Tree*. They wanted to meet us because they knew the book and loved it. That touched our hearts."

Find out more at leeandlow.com/books/zora.html

Fall 1995

GIVING THANKS: A NATIVE AMERICAN GOOD MORNING MESSAGE

by **Chief Jake Swamp**
illustrated by **Erwin Printup, Jr.**

- *Reading Rainbow* selection
- 50 Multicultural Books Every Child Should Know, Cooperative Children's Book Center
- "Choices," Cooperative Children's Book Center

◆ "A simple, tender celebration of good fortune." —*Kirkus Reviews*, pointer

"Its simple, timeless language bears witness to the Native American reverence for the natural world and sense of unity with all living things." —*Publishers Weekly*

Chief Jake Swamp

"One day as I was coming home from my travels, I realized that people in general didn't appear to be thankful, as one should be. This was particularly noticeable to me because in our traditional Mohawk cultural teachings, we give thanks each and every day.

"As children, we are taught to give thanks as soon as we awaken—to be thankful for the arrival of each new day, to honor and give thanks that we are human, to give thanks to Mother Earth and all her special gifts. We give thanks also to the air we breathe, the rains, sun, moon, and stars, and special thanks to our spiritual guides.

"The realization that too many of us were ignoring thankfulness inspired me to write this book so that people from the age of one to one hundred would have thanksgiving as the foundation of their lives. That would be special indeed. I am very happy that Lee & Low understood my vision and that they published *Giving Thanks*. I hope and pray that all the learning institutions that teach our children will continue to use *Giving Thanks* as part of their educational materials."

Erwin Printup, Jr.

"I feel very fortunate to have worked with Chief Swamp to deliver a part of Native American culture to the rest of the world and share the message to give thanks every day instead of once a year as a holiday.

"I have been painting since 1979, and most of my artwork is influenced by my Iroquois culture. Illustrating *Giving Thanks* gave me the chance to share my culture with everybody. The 'Four Winds' is my favorite picture in the book. It shows the symbols of the seasons, the winds that come from the south, north, west, and east, and how the characteristics of the animals pertain to the weather or the winds that are blowing at the time.

"Mostly I used to be by myself doing my artwork, but since the book came out several years ago, I've had the chance to go out and talk with different people. I've been giving seminars for adults and going to schools. It's been great doing shows for the children, talking about the message of *Giving Thanks* and my artwork, and explaining the pictures in the book.

"Sharing of the giving-thanks belief is for everybody."

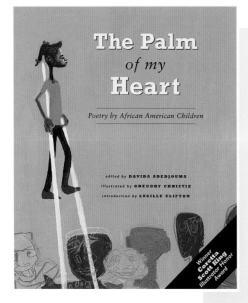

Poetry by African American Children

Fall 1996

THE PALM OF MY HEART:
POETRY BY AFRICAN AMERICAN CHILDREN

edited by **Davida Adedjouma**
illustrated by **R. Gregory Christie**

• Coretta Scott King Illustrator Award Honor
• Reading Magic Award, *Parenting* magazine

"A dazzling glimpse of what it means to be young, gifted, and black."
—*QBR: The Black Book Review*

"African-American children celebrate black creativity, culture, beauty and so much more in profound and moving original poems."
—"Choices," Cooperative Children's Book Center

Davida Adedjouma

"I was inspired to edit *The Palm of My Heart* because the students who wrote the poems needed to see their work in print in order to validate it. I made a small book at a copy shop so each student could have his or her work in book form, and Lee & Low decided to publish the 'Black Is . . .' section of that book.

"The title *The Palm of My Heart* was actually a 'mistake' by the poet. She meant to write 'the palm of my hand,' but it came out 'the palm of my heart,' which I thought was absolutely beautiful—the verse coming from the center, or palm, of her heart. I decided to title the book after that incredible mistake.

"Since the publication of *The Palm of My Heart,* I've done presentations on teaching children how to write, worked on teaching models for schools in Minnesota and New York, and participated in book conferences and signings where I encouraged youngsters to write their own stories and poetry. All this helped lead to the production of my three children's musicals at SteppingStone Theatre in Minnesota, where I first taught students to write."

Gary Spector

R. Gregory Christie

"Lee & Low took a chance on me with *The Palm of My Heart.* I had no portfolio, and I was nervous about doing my first book. But I loved this project because of the opportunity it presented. All the poems are simple and effective. Therefore, for me, the artwork had to be the same. The poems also became a way for me to evaluate the notion of what black really is: black the color, black the people, black the emotional aspect.

"My biggest challenge was to find my mark, to do that first image as a foundation and then build from there. The first piece has to feel good, and usually it's the piece I feel most connected to. It's my messenger—which turned out to be 'Black Hands.'

"Working on the book gave me a greater respect for the power of poetry. In short, I was a shadow of the poems. The poems were a dark background that I was cast upon. Hopefully the viewer will see us both.

"The publication of this book brought my art to the masses. It feels good to use my artwork to educate children."

Find out more at leeandlow.com/books/palm.html

Spring 1997

PASSAGE TO FREEDOM:
THE SUGIHARA STORY
by **Ken Mochizuki**
illustrated by **Dom Lee**

- Notable Children's Books, American Library Association
- Parents' Choice Award
- Jane Addams Children's Book Award Honor
- Pick of the Lists, *American Bookseller*

★ "A stirring story." —*Publishers Weekly*, starred review

"This testament to one man's courage should be read in homes and classrooms across the nation and the world."

—Notable Books for Children, *Smithsonian* magazine

Ken Mochizuki

"During the autumn of 2000, little did I know I had an appointment with history. A teacher in Houston, Texas, had arranged for me to meet a 'Sugihara survivor.' The survivor recalled seeing family photographs of herself as a child, and she had always wondered why there were pictures of her family in Japan during the 1940s and aboard a ship crossing the Pacific Ocean. And why were there Japanese characters written on an old World War II–era visa?

"Around the mid-1990s this woman began hearing about Consul Sugihara and the thousands of visas he issued to Polish Jews in Lithuania to help them escape the Holocaust. She made the connection with those photographs. Further research revealed that she and her family received one of the first ten visas issued by Sugihara, beginning her family's trek across Russia to Japan, and eventually to North America. She was three years old at the time.

"Then she showed me the actual visa. There, on the middle page, were the Japanese characters written by Consul Sugihara with his fountain pen. I had held history in my hands."

Keunhee Lee

Dom Lee

"As an artist, my goal is to achieve a genuine reality through my artwork. In the whole process of illustrating a book, I spend the largest portion of the time researching to ensure the project's authenticity. I try to gather as many references as possible: Photographs, videos, old magazines, clothing, and hats are the kinds of items that I've collected.

"When I interpret the author's words by means of works of art, I do not merely represent a tale. I also try to get into the minds of the main characters in the story and show the reader what the characters are feeling and seeing.

"When I first began my research for *Passage to Freedom,* I knew only a few facts about the Holocaust. But then I visited the Holocaust Memorial Museum in Washington, D.C., and I was shocked by what I saw. I will never forget the impact that museum had on me.

"I was fortunate to have this opportunity to make a tribute to such an important part of history. I also felt a great responsibility for the power of the images I've illustrated."

Find out more at leeandlow.com/books/passage.html

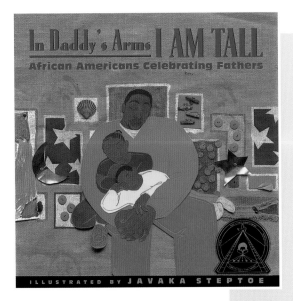

Fall 1997

IN DADDY'S ARMS I AM TALL:
AFRICAN AMERICANS CELEBRATING FATHERS

illustrated by **Javaka Steptoe**

- Coretta Scott King Illustrator Award
- Notable Children's Books, American Library Association
- NAACP Image Award, Outstanding Children's Literary Work
- Texas Bluebonnet Award Masterlist

"[An] inventive, evocative book." —*Kirkus Reviews*

★ "This stunning homage to fathers offers a textured potpourri of voices and visuals." —*Publishers Weekly*, starred review

★ "Javaka Steptoe creates a splendid series of images in mixed media. . . . This promises read-aloud and read-to-share comfort for many readings and rereadings." —*Booklist*, starred review

Javaka Steptoe

Gary Spector

"My first project in the children's book field was *In Daddy's Arms I Am Tall.* It was a special book for me because it celebrates fatherhood in the black family. There are so many stories about the black father never being around, so the black woman has to play the role of both mother and father. These stories are true for many families, but there are also black families in which the father has a strong, active, and positive role. This book celebrates these men and inspires young men to want to be that type of father.

"*In Daddy's Arms* was a long time coming. I have always been an artist. Art was something that I have always done. I watched my mother and father work and learned from them. But at one point I tried to deny my nature by doing other things besides my art. In the end it is the things that we love and love working hard at that give us everything we need and want.

"My father, John Steptoe, who took an active role in my growing up, died when I was seventeen. I have a small, close-knit family in New York, and all but one of the elder men in my family have passed on. I never had a tour guide into manhood. I never had a mentor, and manhood is a scary journey to take especially if you feel you're by yourself. *In Daddy's Arms* was the beginning of this journey, my first big step into manhood. The book made that step less scary. It let me look at manhood and fatherhood, and let me examine the relationship I had with my father and other men.

"My cousins and I are now the elders of the family, and the question we face every day is, what do we have to give to the younger children in our family. So far I have learned that we have to lead by example. We have to be strong and share what we have learned about life. We have to give love and be willing to receive love. We have to never give up helping these children take their first steps into manhood."

Find out more at leeandlow.com/books/daddy.html

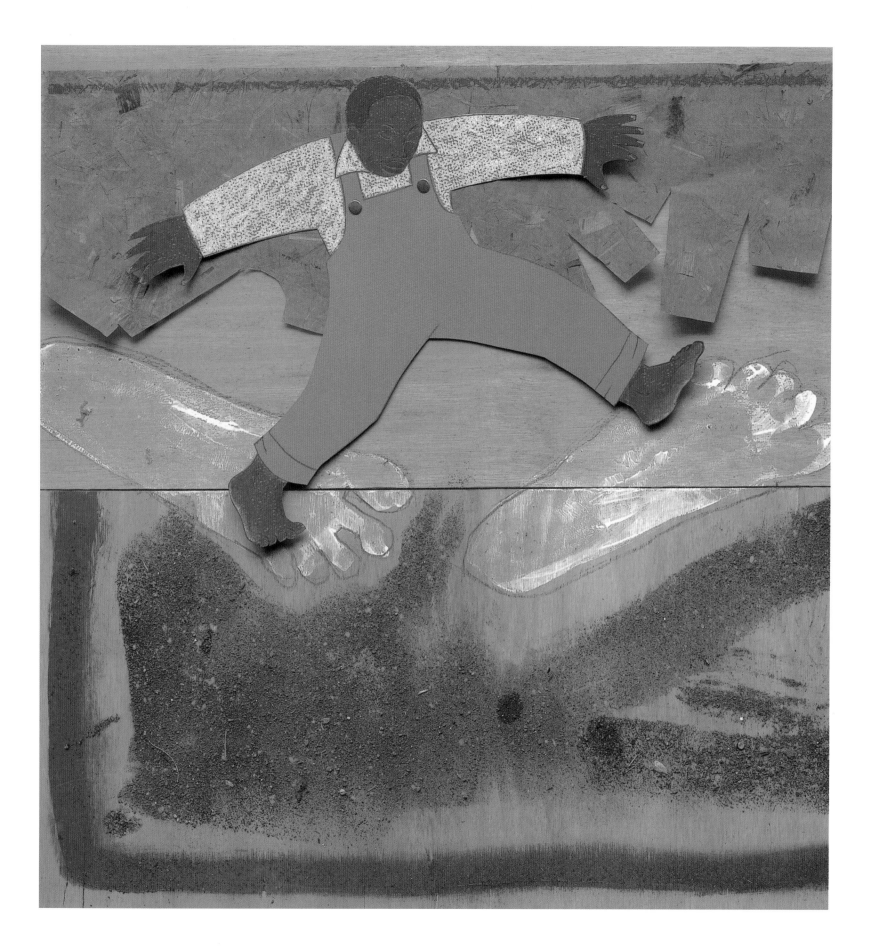

Fall 1998

ELIZABETI'S DOLL

by **Stephanie Stuve-Bodeen**
illustrated by **Christy Hale**

- Ezra Jack Keats New Writer Award
- Notable Children's Books, American Library Association
- Best Books, *School Library Journal*

★ "A little slice of perfection."　　　　*—Publishers Weekly,* starred review

★ "This book is a splendid celebration of life and the power of a child's imagination."　　　　*—School Library Journal,* starred review

◆ "[The story] is quirky but believable, lightly dusted with cultural detail, and features universal emotions in an unusual setting."　*—Kirkus Reviews,* pointer

Stephanie Stuve-Bodeen

"As a Peace Corps volunteer in Tanzania, I spent a week with a Tanzanian family. Their home was tiny and made of mud and sticks, and I would lie in bed at night with the covers over my head, listening to rats rustle around beneath me. For a long time I referred to that time as the worst week of my life.

"Years later, when I started thinking about writing for children, that week came to mind. Around that time some Peace Corps friends came to visit, and someone commented, 'A girl in my village had a rock for a doll.' I remembered how the little girls would do that, and I woke up at 3 A.M. the very next day, sat down at the kitchen table, and wrote the first version of *Elizabeti's Doll*. It happened to be my thirtieth birthday.

"Thinking the story was pretty good, I sent it off to some publishers, and eventually to Lee & Low Books. Within a few months they called to acquire the story, saying it was 'a gem.' And so the worst week of my life resulted in my first published book.

"*Elizabeti's Doll* was truly a gift."

Christy Hale

"*Elizabeti's Doll* always elicited a personal and emotional response from me. Rocks figure strongly into my history. My father 'hales' from Rockport, Massachusetts, an old quarry town. He would haul quarry rocks to our home, and he shaped them into beautiful stone walls and zigzagged a stairway path up our back hill. Just as in *Elizabeti's Doll*, I knew one of the stones was special. It was not a stone at all. It was my pet skunk! I tied a rope around it and walked my pet around the yard.

"This book was different for me as an artist—the first truly sweet illustration project to come my way. It necessitated a softer approach than anything I had done previously. It marked a change stylistically in my work, and I was delighted to hear from Stephanie that Tanzanians she knows felt I had captured their world.

"The success of *Elizabeti's Doll* lies in its simplicity and earnestness, and I've shared it with many of my daughter's friends. The parent of one friend said the story affected her family so strongly that they went through their toys and donated many of them to others more needy."

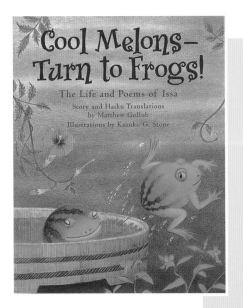

Fall 1998

COOL MELONS—TURN TO FROGS!
THE LIFE AND POEMS OF ISSA

by **Matthew Gollub**

illustrated by **Kazuko G. Stone**

- Fanfare, *The Horn Book Magazine*
- Notable Children's Books, American Library Association
- Notable Children's Books in the English Language Arts, National Council of Teachers of English

★ "This introduction to an eighteenth-century Japanese writer of haiku is as restrained, graceful, and concise as the art form it honors."

—*The Horn Book Magazine*, starred review

"Like the haiku form of poetry itself, here is a book that is all grace and wonder."

—"Choices," Cooperative Children's Books Center

Matthew Gollub

"I consider *Cool Melons—Turn to Frogs!* a sort of meditation on the beauty and fragility of all living things. Describing the sadness and loss that Issa endured in a way helped me mourn a loss of my own. When I was ten years old, my father passed away. At the time I was devastated. Even now, if I read the book from cover to cover, I shed a few tears and remember my dad.

"I first met Kazuko Stone at a convention. We were signing books side-by-side, and I decided to greet her in Japanese. Her eyes opened wide in surprise, and later we exchanged business cards. A month later she wrote to me saying she had loved Issa's poetry since she was a girl, and she asked if I'd be interested in translating some of his haiku.

"Reading passages of *Cool Melons* and some of the haiku in Japanese wins me instant respect among students. The book says to them that no matter what their circumstances, they too are part of the continuum of human experience. This story of a long-ago Japanese poet affirms that people can surmount difficulties and still cherish the miracle of life."

Sally Marr

Gem Stone

Kazuko G. Stone

"When I was a child in Japan, we recited Issa's haiku in school. His subject was often small animals and insects that were familiar to us. Years later, in the United States, I went to the children's poetry section in the library and found that none of the books of haiku were illustrated by a Japanese artist. I decided I wanted to do a book on Issa's haiku to introduce American children to traditional Japanese images and feelings, and to make the illustrations as true to my childhood memories as possible.

"In order to further my understanding of Issa, I visited the last place he lived. It was a small shed, because his house had burned down a year before he died. Issa even wrote a haiku about the ashes that were left after the fire. He found warmth and humor in what remained.

"I once gave a copy of *Cool Melons* to a Japanese person who had lived in the United States a long time. He wrote to me, 'This book made me cry.' Even most westerners feel something of the serenity and simplicity of Japanese culture that I tried to show in the illustrations."

Find out more at leeandlow.com/books/cool.html

STRONG to the HOOP

BY JOHN COY · ILLUSTRATIONS BY LESLIE JEAN-BART

Fall 1999

STRONG TO THE HOOP
by **John Coy**
illustrated by **Leslie Jean-Bart**

- Notable Children's Books, American Library Association
- "Choices," Cooperative Children's Book Center
- Marion Vannett Ridgway Award Illustration Honor

"Cleanly compelling." —*Kirkus Reviews*

"Real-life kids competing on a mythic playing field—that's the message here, but you don't need to understand it in those terms to feel its allure." —*Booklist*

John Coy

"Because I loved basketball so much, I spent thousands of hours practicing on the dirt court in my backyard, at the school playground, and at the YMCA. Later, working on *Strong to the Hoop* reinforced how much I love the game. I wanted to crystallize this into a story for others who share my passion.

"My favorite aspect of the book was the research. I knew there was a noon game at the downtown Y each day. I could always walk over and play for a while. Some days I'd get a sound, some days the right dialogue. Other days I'd just play, but it all was research.

"The publication of this book has opened one door after another. I have worked with teachers and librarians in numerous states, and watching students perform the text as a play for the first time was particularly moving. Lee & Low connected me with the National Basketball Association's Read to Achieve Program, and NBA players have used *Strong to the Hoop* in literacy programs across the country.

"The effects and influences of the book just keep growing, and I have the sense that this is just the beginning."

David Brewster

Matthew Marston

Leslie Jean-Bart

"Illustrating *Strong to the Hoop* was an exciting challenge that completely terrified and utterly intoxicated me at various times during the process.

"From the moment I began working on the project, I was determined to do a 'different' children's book, though I was not sure at first how I was going to make it different. I headed straight to the public library and studied as many types of children's books on a variety of subjects as I could find. Finally I decided that I wanted the illustrations to have two basic effects. First, I wanted them to feel 'real and surreal,' almost like a movie. Second, I wanted the reader/viewer to be able to imagine himself or herself in the story, just as I used to do while reading the fables of Jean de La Fontaine as a child.

"I realized finally to trust my vision and to simply make it happen. Of course it's never that simple. But then again, it is. I find it both a blast and a little unbelievable to see others embrace something that I saw only in my mind's eye and was, to a great extent, a figment of my imagination."

Spring 2000
CRAZY HORSE'S VISION
by **Joseph Bruchac**
illustrated by **S. D. Nelson**

- Notable Children's Books, American Library Association
- Parents' Choice Award
- Reading Magic Award, *Parenting* magazine
- Notable Book for a Global Society, International Reading Association

★ "Inspirational reading." —*Kirkus Reviews,* starred review

"Bruchac has created a memorable tale about Crazy Horse's childhood. . . . Sioux artist Nelson fills the pages with both action and quiet drama."

—*Booklist*

Joseph Bruchac

"The story of Crazy Horse and his quest for a vision to help his people is one I have known for many years. I first read about Crazy Horse as a teenager and then heard stories about him from Lakota and Cheyenne friends when I was in my twenties. Crazy Horse seemed to have lived a life for his *people,* not just for himself, and I thought he was a great role model. I feel very humble when I look at his life.

"My audience, as always, is young readers in general. But I also thought of *Crazy Horse's Vision* as a book that could be very important for American Indian people, both young and old. So many bad books have been written about Indians in general and the Lakota in particular. I wanted this book to counter some of those distorted and untrue stories.

"I think people have connected to this book because it touches something in them—not just a romantic fascination with Indians, but a story of bringing hope out of despair, of finding courage, of wanting to do something for others. Something for all our relations."

John Pflug

S. D. Nelson

"While illustrating *Crazy Horse's Vision*, I was in a constant 'state of inspiration.' At an early age my Lakota mother taught me to admire Crazy Horse, the warrior. Then prior to illustrating the story, I read biographies about him. During the project, I strove for an authentic interpretation of Joseph Bruchac's story while at the same time bringing my own feelings and style to the images.

"One of the greatest challenges I faced was the manner in which I presented the scenes of conflict. Keeping in mind that my audience was children and their parents, I found inspiration in the traditional ledger paintings of the Plains Indians. The bold, colorful, and immediate style seemed to strike a common chord with most people.

"I have always believed that life is a Great Mystery, or what we Lakota call Wakan Tanka. Illustrating this book was an opportunity for me to share my feelings about the Indian Way of Seeing.

"Children have often told me that *Crazy Horse's Vision* is their favorite book. For an illustrator that's a delightful thing to hear! And frankly I am just thrilled with the success of this true-life Native American story."

Find out more at leeandlow.com/books/vision.html

Spring 2002

LOVE TO LANGSTON

by **Tony Medina**
illustrated by **R. Gregory Christie**

- Best Books, *School Library Journal*
- Notable Children's Books in the English Language Arts, National Council of Teachers of English
- One Hundred Titles for Reading and Sharing, New York Public Library

★ "This is a treasure to be read and reread—a splendid work."

—*Kirkus Reviews,* **starred review**

★ "Medina's words stand on their own while they honor the tradition established by Hughes. . . . [Christie's] vibrant illustrations . . . invite readers into the world of sharecroppers, ocean liners, and libraries." —*School Library Journal,* **starred review**

Tony Medina

"When I was in high school I came across a copy of Langston Hughes's *Selected Poems.* On the cover was a picture of Langston sitting at his typewriter, staring over his shoulder at the reader, me. I had never seen a brown man on the cover of a book, and it made me feel good. Then I started reading some of the poems, which talked about Harlem and jazz and

everyday people who resembled my family. Langston immediately became one of my favorite poets.

"When it was time for Langston Hughes to turn one hundred years old, I thought it would be great to pay tribute to him with a book in verse. It would be as if Langston were communicating directly with today's young readers, and they would learn about an important American writer who not only influenced me, but generations of people of all backgrounds.

"People of all ages love *Love to Langston*, but children are the best audience. They are so smart and funny, and they respond to the vibrancy and emotional honesty of the book. That I am positively influencing young readers gives the greatest pleasure and inspiration to me."

R. Gregory Christie

"I was drawing before I could speak. By the time I started school, it became the best way for me to communicate. Drawing felt like the natural way to connect to people. It helped me connect then and continues to do so today.

"I knew that Langston Hughes was a talented poet to be revered, but only after hearing his story from Tony Medina did I feel an intense desire to put his biography into images. Langston seemed to be a private individual who was also encircled by friends. His lifestyle as an artist and friend to his peers immediately connected me to him.

"My big challenge was to find the right style for the book. I knew the poems were often melancholic, but there was also joy and honesty. I settled on a style inspired by the work of William H. Johnson, a Harlem Renaissance artist who may have been in the same circles as Langston.

"Often I meet people who are really excited about the innovative way the book portrays Langston's life. The book has also inspired me to further educate myself about historical figures and the overlooked achievements of great individuals."

Fall 2002

THE POT THAT JUAN BUILT

by **Nancy Andrews-Goebel**

illustrated by **David Diaz**

- Notable Children's Books, American Library Association
- Best Books, *School Library Journal*
- Children's Book Award, International Reading Association
- Best Books of the Year, *Parenting* magazine

★ "[A]n inventive and engrossing biography."

—*Publishers Weekly*, starred review

"Just as Andrews-Goebel's poems demonstrate the cumulative nature of artistic creation, so Diaz's images reveal the way finished art integrates multiple levels of detail into a coordinated whole."

—*The New York Times Book Review*

Nancy Andrews-Goebel

The Photo Shop / Sharon Ward

"Juan's nearly mythological life story was one that begged to be told, especially to children. I'm just delighted that while I was living in Mata Ortiz I had the opportunity to become familiar enough with the village, the pottery, and the Quezada family to write *The Pot That Juan Built.*

"The initial audience I had in mind was America's diverse population of young readers, but I am pleased that I was also able to create a book that has been universally appealing. Discussing the book with my friend, I joked about leaving out the cow manure part of the pottery process. 'Why?' my friend said. 'Kids love poop!' So I included what are now my favorite lines in the book.

"*The Pot That Juan Built* is multicultural for me because of the mixing of influences from a variety of cultures, both contemporary and past, that are an essential part of Juan Quezada's life story.

"When Juan saw the book, he told me, 'I like the book very much, everything about it! The pictures are lovely. I think a lot of people will want to have this book.' Nothing could please me more."

David Diaz

"I have been a ceramic potter for nine years and *The Pot That Juan Built* resonated with me immediately. This is a fascinating story. It's amazing that Juan Quezada went to such lengths to fulfill his craft.

"When I first saw the story, I liked the way it was structured. I liked the repetition, and I had a pretty clear image of what I wanted to do right from the beginning. The biggest challenge then was combining the art with the two approaches of the text, trying to make all those things work together on the same page and throughout the entire book.

"While illustrating the story, I became much more aware of Juan's work and the dedication potters like him put into their art. I think that's inspiring—that people will create their art almost at any cost. There is a passion that drives them, and that's something to aspire to—to be driven to such a degree, to find your voice in your work. Juan's pottery has such a long tradition, and because of its beauty and simplicity, it has found an international market.

"If you create beautiful things, they will find their audience."

NEW VOICES AWARD

In 2000, we established our annual New Voices Award for a first picture book manuscript by a writer of color. Here are the winners so far.

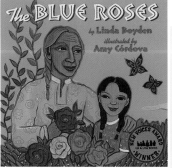

LINDA BOYDEN

AMY CÓRDOVA

JPB Photography

Roland Jacobs

THERESE ON LOUIE   SULING WANG

2000 Winner, published Spring 2002
THE BLUE ROSES
by **Linda Boyden**
illustrated by **Amy Córdova**

- "Choices," Cooperative Children's Book Center
- Paterson Prize for Books for Young People

"A gentle story of family ties, loss and dreams."—*Kirkus Reviews*

Find out more at leeandlow.com/books/blueroses.html

2000 Honor, published Fall 2002
RAYMOND'S PERFECT PRESENT
by **Therese On Louie**
illustrated by **Suling Wang**

- "Choices," Cooperative Children's Book Center

"A lovely tale of triumph over the adversity of illness and limited resources."   —*School Library Journal*

Find out more at leeandlow.com/books/raymond.html

2000 Honor, published Fall 2002
GHOSTS FOR BREAKFAST
by **Stanley Todd Terasaki**
illustrated by **Shelly Shinjo**

- Notable Books for Children, *Smithsonian* magazine

"A perfect blend of humor and suspense."   —*Kirkus Reviews*

Find out more at leeandlow.com/books/ghosts.html

2001 Winner, published Fall 2003
JANNA AND THE KINGS
by **Patricia Smith**
illustrated by **Aaron Boyd**

A young girl learns to keep her grandfather's memory alive by rediscovering their special place.

Find out more at leeandlow.com/books/janna.html

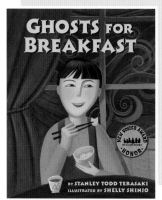

STANLEY TODD TERASAKI   SHELLY SHINJO

PATRICIA SMITH   AARON BOYD